The Best
Job for Scooter

by Ryan Fadus   illustrated by Barry Gott

 HOUGHTON MIFFLIN   BOSTON

Mr. and Mrs. Hall's dog had four puppies.
One puppy had short brown fur and white paws.
He ran around in circles and barked. Mr. Hall
named him Scooter.

The Halls gave away the puppies one by
one—all except Scooter. For some reason, no one
seemed to want him.

"Well," said Mr. Hall, "we can't keep Scooter. We'll just have to find a job for him."

"I know," Mrs. Hall said. "I saw an ad in the paper. Steve is looking for a watchdog for his store. Let's take Scooter there."

Steve at the store agreed to take Scooter. He showed Scooter where to stand guard. Soon Scooter was tired of standing. He didn't like being a watchdog. Scooter lay down on the floor.

Steve heard snores coming from the front of the store. Scooter was fast asleep! Even when Steve got near Scooter, the dog didn't lift his head.

"A sleeping watchdog!" Steve cried. "This will never do." And he returned Scooter to Mr. and Mrs. Hall.

5

"So you don't like being a watchdog," said Mr. Hall. "I have another idea. The police department is looking for a dog to train. We'll try that."

The next morning, Mr. Hall brought Scooter to Officer Armas.

Officer Armas put Scooter in the back of the police car and off they went. Scooter enjoyed the ride. He put his nose near the open window. He smelled lots of exciting things. He was sorry when the ride was over.

At the training center, Officer Armas tried to work with Scooter. She called, "Scooter, sit. Scooter, stay. Scooter, come."

But Scooter had a hard time paying attention to the commands. He kept thinking about the police car and the good smells.

After a week, Officer Armas returned Scooter to Mr. and Mrs. Hall.

"Scooter is a nice dog," she told Mr. Hall. "But he doesn't want to do police work. All he wants to do is ride in the police car all day."

So the Halls needed another plan.

"Do you remember my friend Frank?" asked Mrs. Hall. "He owns a sheep farm."

"I forgot about Frank," Mr. Hall said. "Maybe Scooter would like to work with sheep."

Mr. Hall dropped Scooter off at the farm the next day.

Frank started to train Scooter to herd the sheep. But Scooter didn't listen. He would hide behind a tree or a bush. He wanted to play.

Finally, Frank found Scooter swimming in the duck pond. This was the last straw!

"You don't want to be a herding dog," said Frank. So Frank took Scooter back to Mr. and Mrs. Hall.

The Halls were worried. They didn't know what job Scooter would like.

One day, Mrs. Simm and her son, Bart, came to see the Halls. "My mom said I could get a dog for my birthday," said Bart.

Mr. and Mrs. Hall looked at each other. Then Mr. Hall got Scooter from the backyard.

"How about this dog?" he asked Bart.

Bart looked at Scooter. "He looks like a good dog," Bart said.

"What does he like to do?" Mrs. Simm asked.

Mrs. Hall answered with a smile. "Scooter likes to ride in the car. He likes to play and swim. And he likes to sleep."

"He sounds like the perfect dog for me," said Bart. "Can we keep him, Mom?"

"Yes, Bart," Mrs. Simm replied. "He'll make a wonderful pet for you."

And so the Halls finally found the best job
for Scooter.